U0164166

詩中有真味

Poetic Flavor in Poetry

許其正主編

張紫涵英譯

《華文現代詩》五周年同仁詩選

華文現代詩叢刊
文史哲出版社印行

國家圖書館出版品預行編目資料

詩中有真味= Poetic Flavor in Poetry / 許其
正主編・張紫涵英譯.-- 初版.-- 臺北市：
文史哲，民 109.07
  頁：　公分　（華文現代詩叢刊；2）
中英對照
ISBN 978-986-314-519-6（平裝）

863.51   109010032

華文現代詩叢刊　②

詩 中 有 眞 味
Poetic Flavor in Poetry

主　編　者：許　　　　其　　　　正
英　譯　者：張　　　　紫　　　　涵
出　版　者：文　史　哲　出　版　社
　　　　http://www.lapen.com.tw
　　　　e-mail:lapen@ms74.hinet.net
登記證字號：行政院新聞局版臺業字五三三七號
發　行　人：彭　　　　正　　　　雄
發　行　所：文　史　哲　出　版　社
印　刷　者：文　史　哲　出　版　社
　　　　臺北市羅斯福路一段七十二巷四號
　　　　郵政劃撥帳號：一六一八〇一七五
　　　　電話886-2-23511028・傳真886-2-23965656

實價新臺幣二八〇元

二〇二〇年（民一〇九）七月初版

序

詩中有真味

許其正

　　來了！來了！我們來了。我們從四面八方來了。我們或從事士農工商軍公教。我們有男有女。我們這一群，或年紀已大，大都已經退休，有些仍在職，最大年紀甚至已八十。我們興致勃勃地聚集過來，聚集在《華文現代詩》裡。當年甚至我們自己都說最多只有二年，從 2014 年起，到現在，卻已五周年。我們或有不同意見，卻能磨合，異中求同，大家齊心協力向前走，雖然或者汗流浹背，氣喘如牛，卻走得興緻勃勃，有聲有色。

　　我們為的是什麼？沒得話說，為了詩。

　　我們都是詩的愛好者，甚至說都是詩人。

　　我們都認知，我們活在人世間，不是只求物質的享受，更需要柔性文化的滋養，尤其是詩。詩之於我們是最重要的，那是心靈的滋補品，尤其身處現代科技極度發達的時代，身處高樓大廈的都市中，望眼都是灰矇矇的空間和一堵堵牆壁，極少綠色養眼的景致，極少柔性的東西來調適。只有科技是不行的。冷冷的，硬梆梆的，死氣沉沉的，枯燥無味的，沒有情趣的，沒有人性和人文的，這樣單調的日子，我們怎麼過活？心靈要往哪裡寄託？這樣單調的日子，我們更需要柔性的東西來滋潤，來調和。最上選的就是詩了。

　　從創刊起，迄今已五周年了。我們都想擴大影響，讓我們的努力沒有白費，所以有《點將錄》的製作，有一些活動，有本書同仁中英對照詩選的出版。我們集合了編輯群的詩予以英譯，以中英對照的方式來和讀者相見面，也或許可以做拋磚引玉的工作，讓我們的詩可以推出去，讓全世界都見到我們的詩，賞讀我們的詩，一起來互動，提升人類的心靈和世界的文化。

　　詩中有真味。詩中有真趣。讓我們都沉浸在詩的氛圍裡，共沐在和平真情中，過美好的日子，歡樂的日子。

Preface

Poetic Flavor in Poetry

By Hsu Chicheng

Yes, here we are! From all directions and different corners of the world. We are differently engaged, in agriculture or industry or business or teaching, inclusive of men and women. As a motley group of senior writers, most of us are tired, the most advanced in age is over 80. With great interest and gusto, we gather together by the periodical of *Modern Chinese Poetry*. When we made the plan for two years, yet five years have passed since 2014. Though our opinions vary, we try to seek commonness among differences, so as to make concerted efforts for a bright future. In spite of efforts and sweat of the brow, we walk on, bubbling over with great enthusiasm.

What, if asked, is our purpose? For poetry, of course.

We are all ardent lovers of poetry, and we are poets.

It is common knowledge that we, in the mortal world, do not only pursue material pleasures, but also we need to be nurtured by soft culture, particularly poetry. For us, poetry is the most important, for it is the tonic for the soul. In the age of fast development in science and technology, we are living in cities of tall buildings, grey space filled with tall walls which obstruct beautiful scenery. It does us no good if only with science and technology and without soft things to condition us. How can we bear to live, in such cold, dreary, cheerless days without humanity and humanistic cares? Where does our soul rest? Our monotonous days should be enlivened by soft and tender things, among which the best is poetry.

From the founding date of the periodical, five years have passed. It is our common wish to expand the influence, in order for our efforts not to be made in vain; therefore, we take some actions, including the publication of this Chinese-English version of poetry by my colleagues. We hope that this collection can cast a brick to attract jade, for our poetry to be shared by readers across the world, so as to join hands in uplifting human spirit and enhancing world culture.

Poetic flavor in poetry, as well as interest and beauty in poetry. Let us delight in poetry, bathing ourselves in peace and friendly emotion, so as to enjoy our beautiful and happy days.

詩中有眞味

― 華文現代詩同仁中英詩選

許其正主編　張紫涵英譯

目　次

主編簡介

　　許其正，台灣當代傑出的詩人、作家、翻譯家。臺灣屏東縣人，1939 年生，東吳大學法學士；曾任編輯、記者、軍法官、教師兼部分文學社團負責人、指導教師等；現在已退休。

　　許氏自小對文藝及寫作具有興趣，於 1960 年開始發表作品，以新詩與散文為主，多寫鄉土、田園、大自然，歌頌人生光明面，勉人奮發向上；已出版 26 本著作，其中 14 本為詩集；作品被譯成英文、日文、希臘文、蒙古文、希伯來文、俄文、法文、葡萄牙文與馬爾他文，被選入近百種選集，詩、散文及劇本曾多次得獎，曾獲國際詩歌翻譯研究中心頒發榮譽文學博士學位及 2004 年最佳國際詩人，美國世界文化藝術學院頒發榮譽文學博士，國際作家藝術家協會頒發榮譽人文博士及英譯中最佳翻譯，希臘札斯特朗文學會頒發紀念獎，黎巴嫩耐吉·阿曼文學獎頒發詩歌榮譽獎，曾被提名為 2014 年度諾貝爾文學獎候選人。

　　他現在專事閱讀與寫作，作品以中、英、日、希臘、蒙古等語文，在國內外報紙、雜誌發表，並兼任《大海洋詩雜誌》&《世界詩人》顧問及《華文現代詩》編委，國際作家藝術家協會會員，希臘札斯特朗文學會榮譽會員。

About the Chief Editor

Hsu Chicheng, a distinguished contemporary Taiwanese poet, writer and translator, native of Pingtung County, Taiwan; born in 1939; LLB of Soochow University. He was once an editor, a journalist, a military judge, a teacher as well as part-time director, leading member or guiding teacher to some mass organizations of art and literature. He has now retired.

From his childhood, he is fond of literature and writing. Since 1960 he started to publish his works, most of his works are poems and prose, mainly depicting native land, idyllic life and nature, singing the praise of the brilliant side of human experience, based on humanity to encourage people to brace themselves up and be bent on doing good deeds. He has published 26 books including 14 collections of poems. Many of his poems have been translated into English, Japanese, Greek, Mongolian, Hebrew, Russian, French, Portuguese, Maltese and recorded in near hundred selections of poems. His poems, prose works and plays have won prizes for times. He was conferred an honorary doctorate of literature and one of the international best poets 2004 by The International Poetry Translation And Research Centre, was conferred also an honorary doctorate of literature by The U.S. World Academy of Arts and Culture, was conferred also a doctor honoris causa in humanities as well as the best translator from English to Chinese by The International Writers and Artists Association and was presented the commemorative prize by Literary Club "Xasteron", Greece, was presented also the honour prize by Naji Naaman's Literary prizes, Lebanon. Moreover, he was nominated for Nobel Prize in Literature, 2014.

He now specializes in reading and writing. Most of his poems are published in Chinese, English, Greek, Japanese or Mongolian both at home and abroad. He is at present the part-time adviser of *Large Ocean Quarterly & The World Poets Quarterly*, editor of *Chinese Modern Poetry Quarterly*. He is member of International Writers and Artists Association, honorary member of Literature Club "Xasteron", Greece.

英譯簡介

張紫涵，女，1994 年生。中南大學英語學士，美國維克森林大學（Wake Forest University）翻譯碩士，現任教於中國民航大學外國語學院。研究方向：文學翻譯與創作。發表學術論文 3 篇，發表詩歌、散文創作等 30 餘首/篇，發表譯文、譯詩數百篇/首。漢譯英著作有：《重慶第一關——青木關》（合譯）、《西可短詩選》（合譯）等。多次獲得文學創作獎。

About the Translator in English

Zhang Zihan, female, was born in 1994. She got her bachelor's degree in English from Central South University and her master's degree in interpreting and translation studies from Wake Forest University of the United States. Now she is teaching at the Foreign Languages College of Civil Aviation University in China, Tianjin. Her research area is literary translation and writing, and she has published 3 academic papers, over 30 poems/essays and hundreds of translated articles / poems. In addition, she has published 2 books of Chinese-English translation: Qingmuguan Pass — The First Pass of Chongqing and Selected Short Poems of Xi Ke. She has won a number of prizes in literary writing competitions.

林錫嘉詩選

詩人簡介

林錫嘉，台灣嘉義人，一九三九年生，台北工專畢，曾任台灣肥料公司工程師，並任《台肥月刊》總編輯，現已退休。

一九八二年二月起創台灣第一部《年度散文選》（九歌版），自該年至一九九八年，其間十八年為推動台灣現代散文之獨立不遺餘力。

一九八〇年起任國軍新文藝研究會召集人，多次帶散文作家群走遍台灣，寫遍台灣。一九八六年首次送書到金門前線，並專訪金門前線建設，出版金門散文專書《碉堡與古厝》。

一九八一年起擔任國軍文藝金像獎散文類評審工作到二〇一一年，另應多所大學文學獎單位之聘擔任文學獎評審；應聘擔任聯合報系「台灣省巡迴文藝營」及「台灣區省立師範學院暑期文藝研習會」散文講座。

一九九九年應聘擔任「台北市張道藩圖書館」駐館作家。

二○一三年十一月與文史哲出版社彭正雄社長及詩友多人籌
辦《華文現代詩季刊》，於二○一四年五月創刊號正式發行，
出任總編輯。

　　詩創作有《親情詩集》、《竹頭集》等五本，散文集有《屬
於山的日子》、《六六集》等四本，翻譯有《流浪者及其欣賞》
等五本；主編九歌版《年度散文選》十八年，《耕雲的手——
散文理論與實踐》等。

Selected Poems of Lin Hsichia

About the Poet

Lin Hsichia was born in 1939 in Jiayi of Taiwan. He was graduated from the Industrial College of Taipei, and has been engineer of Taiwan Fertilizer Company, while assuming editor-in-chief of *Taifei Monthly*, now he is tired.

Since February, 1982, he originated the first collection in Taiwan entitled *Annual Selection of Prose Pieces*, and up to 1998, he has not spared his efforts in the independent development of prose in Taiwan.

Since 1980 he was convener of the Research Society of New Literature, and for many times he has led the group of Taiwan writers in touring Taiwan for literary inspiration. In 1986, for the first time he sent books to the frontline of Kinmen while making an exclusive interview of the construction of Kinmen frontline. He has published a collection of prose pieces written in Kinmen entitled *Fortifications and Old-age Houses*.

From 1981, he undertook the appraisal of prose pieces prize of the Literary Prizes until 2011. In addition, he has been invited by many universities to be the judge of many literary prizes, and invited by the United Newspaper to be the lecturer on art and literature.

In 1999 he was engaged by the Taipei Zhang Daofan Library to be the specially invited writer. In November 2013, together with Peng Cheng Hsiung, president of a publishing house and other poets-friends, he founded *Chinese Modern Poetry Quarterly*, which was issued in May, 2014, and he is the editor-in-chief.

He has published 5 poetry collections, such as *Poems on Family Emotion* and *Poems about Bamboos*, 4 collections of prose pieces, such as *The Days Which Belong to the Mountain* and *Collection of Six and Six*, 5 translated works such as *The Wanderer and Appreciation*, and he has been the editor of *Annual Selection of Prose Pieces* for 18 years, as well as *The Hands Tilling the Clouds — the Theory and Practice of Prose*, etc.

淡水河口黃昏三嘆

一嘆　淡水河口的黃昏

淡水河口
咬不住夕陽
只好把瑰麗的波光雲彩
披在身上
黯然離去

再嘆　河口一孤鳥

河口一隻孤飛的海鳥
淡淡薄薄的影子
牠不知道，已
給河口帶來幾分淒美

Three Sighs by Tamsui at Dusk

The First Sigh: Dusk of Tamsui

The Tamsui

Fails to bite the setting sun

And has to put on the brilliant

Waves and rosy clouds

And leave in dejection

The Second Sigh: a Lonely Bird

By the river there is a lonely flying sea bird

His thin shadow

He does not know, that

It has brought a touch of melancholy to the river

三嘆 吻別

而此黃昏時刻
海與淡水河
輕輕吻別的浪花
邀魚兒共舞

陪銀杏站在岳鹿書院窗前

遠從宋代
運來一車金楓
悄悄倒在岳鹿山上

遠從宋時
錄好朱熹教學的
吟誦聲
隱隱在山麓林間

這裡不允許
喧嘩
除了金楓吟詩

The Third Sigh: Kissing Goodbye

At this moment of dusk
The sea and Tamsui
The sprays gently kissing goodbye
Invite the fish to dance together

Standing before the Window of Yuelu Academy Together with Gingko Trees

From Song Dynasty
A cartful of golden maple leaves has been carried here
Secretly it has been dumped in the Yuelu Mountain

In remote Song Dynasty
The teaching of Zhu Xi
Has been recorded
Dimly in the woods of deer

Here it is forbidden
To make noises
Except for golden maple leaves declaiming poems

這裡不允許
喧嘩
除了銀杏唱詞兒

這裡，用金楓煮熟
所有的歷史
鏤之以碑
　　以匾
　　以楹聯
戰塵啊！
你並不是歷史唯一的重量

擠過重重學子的肩膀
靜靜的
陪銀杏站在講堂窗前
諦聽書聲
且也把腳印輕輕踩下

Here it is forbidden
To make noises
Except for gingko singing songs

Here, with golden maple leaves to boil
All history
To carve a tablet
    A horizontal inscribed board
     A couplet hung on the columns of a hall
Oh war dust!
You are not the only weight of history

Squeezing over the students' shoulders
Silently
Together with gingko standing before the classroom window
Listen to the reading of books
And gently step down

長城，怎麼謠

妳握著山海關那頭
我拉住嘉峪關這端
這麼長的繩
忽而升起躍過峻嶺
忽而低盪至谷底

左腳才從秦國的山谷躍起
右腳已蹬上盛唐峰頂
任憑　　起又落
　　　　落再起

秦起　　秦落
　　漢起　　漢落
唐起　　唐落

我們的思念
走過繩的背脊
纏綿

親愛的啊！
我會堅定拉住嘉峪關的風沙
妳可要緊握住山海關的冰雪

The Great Wall, How to Ode

You grasp one end of Shanhai Pass
I get the other end of Jiayu Pass
So long a rope
Now rises over the mountains
Then down into the valley bottom

The left feet up from the mountain valley of Qin Kingdom
The right feet onto the height of Tang Dynasty
Let it be　rising and falling
　　　　　Falling and rising

Qin rising　　Qin falling
　Han rising　　Han falling
Tang rising　　Tang falling

Our yearning
Walks over ridge of the rope
Meandering

Oh my dear!
I will hold fast to the winds & sands of Jiayu Pass
You shall hold fast to the ice and snow of Shanhai Pass

詩人媽媽

母親在巷口擺肉粽攤，熱騰騰的肉粽香氣在整條巷子裡流動。

我寫詩也很多年了，心裡一直想為母親寫一首詩。

而每年端午，總是為紀念詩人屈原，在各地辦慶祝活動。眾多「詩人」嘴裡吃著肉粽，一邊還吟誦著詩！

今年的詩人節又到了，我七十歲的雙手，捧著熱騰騰的粽子，沒有去想什麼屈原，也沒有想什麼詩，只從心底挖出當年綁的粽子，慢慢剝開粽葉，一陣肉粽香撲鼻而來，看著一粒粒白玉般的米粒，忽然變成母親撫育我的詩句，我伸出雙手擁抱粽子香入懷，竟然發現啊，母親才是一位真正的詩人。

Poet Mama

Mother sets a stall in the entrance of the alley. The scent of the hot rice dumpling is flowing in the whole alley.

I have written poems for many years, and I want to write a poem for my mother continuously from the very beginning.

And during Dragon Boat Festival every year, in memory of Qu Yuan the poet, there are celebrations everywhere. Numerous "Poets" eat the rice dumplings, and even to declaim the poems.

The Dragon Boat Festival is coming again this year. I hold with both my seventy years old hands the hot steaming rice dumplings, neither thinking of Qu Yuan, nor of poems, only dig the dumplings made then from the bottom of my heart, separating the leaves slowly. A spell of scent of the rice dumplings assails my nostrils. Looking at the rice like one after another white jade, they suddenly change into the sentences with which my mother nurtured me. I stretch my hands to embrace the scent of the rice dumplings, and unexpectedly find that only my mother is the true poet.

(Translated by Hsu ChiCheng)

不安的孕婦

公園，一個不安的孕婦
凝望著擾攘的街道
她畏縮在
都市的一個角落

肚子裡，有不規律心跳
醫生斷定
這孩子的存活率不高

灰暗的土地裡也不再有心跳
可憐的孕婦挺著一肚子孤寂
她將變得一無所有
只剩那一雙無助的眼睛
失神的望著
這擾攘不安的島

A Pregnant Woman Who is Uneasy

In the park, a pregnant woman who is uneasy
Gazes at the chaotic street
She shrinks
In a corner of the city

There is no law of heartbeat in her belly
The doctor diagnosed that
The child's survival rate was not high

There is also no heartbeat again on the earth
The poor pregnant woman holds out all her solitariness
She will have nothing to her name
Just a pair of helpless eyes
Gazing the riot island
With absent-minded

(Translated by Hsu ChiCheng)

彭正雄詩選

詩人簡介

彭正雄 Peng Cheng Hsiung，
1939 年生，投入出版事業迄今
58 寒暑。現任文史哲出版社
（The Liberal Arts Press）發行
人、華文現代詩社（Chinese
Modern Poetry Quarterly）發行
人、臺灣出版協會（The
Publishers Association of
Taiwan）副理事長、臺灣數位出
版聯盟協會常務監事、中華民國
新詩學會（Chinese Poetry
Society）常務理事、中國文藝協會理事、臺北市中庸實踐學會理
事長。畢業於臺北市立商校。

先後任職經歷於臺灣學生書局經理、編輯、傳記文學出版社
編輯、文史哲雜誌（The Liberal Arts Magazine）總編輯、教育部
高教評鑑中心（Higher Education Evaluation & Accreditation

Council of Taiwan）、95 年度大學校院系所評鑑委員、國立臺中
圖 92 年《書香遠傳》（Book Boom Magazine）評選諮詢評委。

　　專長領域為：古籍圖書版本目錄學、古籍線裝及圖書裝幀裱
技術、電腦 Word 編排書籍等。　　　　　　注：圖＝圖書館

Selected Poems of
Peng Cheng Hsiung

About the Poet

　　Peng Cheng Hsiung was born in 1939, and has been
engaged in the publishing career for 58 years. Now he is the
issuer of The Liberal Arts Press and Chinese Modern Poetry
Quarterly, vice president of The Publishers Association of
Taiwan, standing president of Taiwan Digital Publishing
Association, standing president of Chinese Poetry Society,
president of China Literature Association, and president of
Taipei Zhongyong Practice Society. He was graduated from the
Business School of Taipei.

Successively he has been manager and editor of Taiwan Students Books Bureau, editor of Biographical Literature Press, editor-in-chief of The Liberal Arts Magazine, member of Higher Education Evaluation & Accreditation Council of Taiwan, 1995 appraisal member of university education, and appraisal member of National Taizhong Library 1992 Book Boom Magazine, etc.

His specialty is: ancient books bibliography, thread-bound ancient books and techniques for books adornment, computer Word for books editing, etc.

詩刊是另類的存在

詩人努力採擷如花的文字，
以腦汁釀造成蜜。
它收集這些各色花蜜，
提供讀者品味欣賞。
你若覺得甜，
它就覺得值。

百合在山坡盛開，
它探訪那抹純潔，
讓美麗得到展現。

幽蘭在深谷綻放，
它搜尋那股清香。
讓芬芳散播更遠更久。

年輕世代的羞澀與爆衝，
需要抒解救贖，

Poetry Periodical Is a Special Existence

The poets make efforts to pick flowery words,
With cerebral juice to produce honey.
It collects various flowery honey,
For the readers to taste and appreciate.
If you feel it sweet,
It feels worthwhile.

Lilies bloom on mountain slopes,
To visit the pure white,
For beauty to be exhibited.

Orchids blossom in the remote deep valley,
In search of the scent.
For it to be spread far and wide.

The coy and drive during the youth,
Need to be saved and solved,

它鼓勵了一首詩，
讓青春明媚而純真。

銀髮族走過荊棘的歷練，
需要榮光印記，
它肯定了一首詩，
可以封存美好回憶。

當一個人打過美好的仗，
需要標誌紀念，
它支持了一首首好詩，
作為每個人戰勝自己的勳章。

它也許沒有雨露滋潤大地的力量，
它也許沒有春風吹醒大地的力量，
但它至少有那麼一扇窗，
讓寫詩的，讀詩的，
可以看見窗外有藍天，
可以讓想像飛向海闊天空。

就算沒有太陽照耀溫暖大地的力量，
但它緊緊守著僅僅一點的飄搖燭光，

It has encouraged a poem,

For youth to be fair and innocent.

The silver-streaked have experienced briers and brambles,

In need of a glorious print,

It has confirmed a poem,

Which can conceal a beautiful memory.

When a person has fought a beautiful battle,

And needs a symbol for memory,

It has supported one after another good poem,

As the medal to conquer oneself.

Perhaps it has no power to nourish the great earth,

Perhaps it has no power for spring wind to awaken the earth,

But at least it has a window,

For poetry writing and poetry reading,

To be able to see the blue sky without the window,

For imagination to soar to the boundless blue sky.

Even if without the sun's power to warm the great earth,

But it only keeps a bit flickering candlelight,

只要那光還亮著，
希望，就存在著。

它，就是如此存在著，
絕對謙卑，
卻又無可取代的頑強堅持，
極度渺小，
卻又無可救藥的自信樂觀，
它，一本詩刊，
真的是非常另類的存在。

So long as the light is bright,
There is hope.

Thus, it exists,
Absolutely humble,
But irreplaceably stubborn and persistent,
Extremely tiny,
Yet hopelessly confident and optimistic,
It, a poetry periodical,
Really a very special existenc.

爺孫兩樣情

丙申長孫首領雙俸

甲午越二載，兒孫為爺賀年

端坐高椅接大孫拜年

阿公驚喜獲長孫大紅包

首於中華甲午，詩壇創世紀誕生

江河長流，喜見又甲午六十大慶

民國第二甲午，華文幼詩社周歲

莊嚴又一甲午，創世紀六十大壽

印行二車詩書冊以致敬

Grandfather and Grandson Different

The oldest grandson gets two salaries first time in the year of
　　Bing-sing
Two years after Jiawu, the grandson celebrates New Year for
　　his grandfather
Sitting in a grand chair he receives ceremony from his
　　grandson
He is pleasantly surprised to receive a red packet from his
　　grandson

In Jiawu years, the creation age of poetry was born
River runs long, we are happy to welcome the 60th anniversary

The second Jiawu year of the Republic, the first anniversary
of Chinese poetry society
Another Jiawu year, the 60th anniversary of the creation age
Two cartloads of books have been printed to pay homage

爺 & 孫

前一刻
帶著初辦詩刊，為著老詩刊賀壽
新生孫輩求教資深祖父級

後一刻
端坐高椅接受孫兒拜年賀禮
寬慰後輩不負親恩

忽而　裝萌賣小
忽而　倚老賣老

不是雙面人的長袖善舞
而是川劇變臉的功夫
不是人生如戲
而是戲如人生多樣的際遇

Grandfather & Grandson

In the former moment
With the new poetry periodical, to congratulate on old poetry
　　periodicals
The new-born grandchildren ask help from their senior
　　grandparents

The next moment
They sit in grand chairs to receive homage from their
　　grandchildren
To comfort the later generations for not forgetting the favors
　　received

Now　some play cute
Then　some play old

Not that the double-faced can dance with long sleeves

But the kongfu of faces changing in Sichuan Opera

Not that life is a play

But that the play is as varied as human life

網路窺視

有人需要被人注意
找機會表現，得到了萬眾矚目
有人喜歡注意別人
窺視的樂趣，撫慰了寂寞窘迫
喜歡表現的人，和喜歡窺視的人
就像凸出的榫頭，和凹進的榫眼
成就了完美的組合

有人藉由網路窺視
也就有人故意在網路上洩漏
鏡頭前的吃喝玩樂，盡量優雅
試圖引起仰慕，遐想
刻意營造若隱若現的虛虛實實
時而釋放一些訊息，滿足你
時而保留一些線索，撩撥你
努力的呈現，渴望被注視
小心翼翼的遮掩，害怕被看透

Network Peeping

Some need to be noticed
To find a chance to exhibit themselves, and get attention from
    myriads of people
Some like to pay attention to other people
The joy of peeping, has comforted straitened loneliness
Those who like to exhibit themselves, and those who like peeping
Like the protruding wedge, and the caved-in mortise
And perfect combination is fulfilled

Some peep by network
And some intentionally leak something on the network
Eating and drinking and playing for fun before the lens, try
to be elegant
Attempt to draw admiration, fantasy
Purposefully create some dim and apparent reality and falsity
Now some message is released, to satisfy you
Then some clues are kept, to tantalize you
Efforts have been made to exhibit, yearn to be noticed
Cover up cautiously, afraid to be seen through

窺視者的胃口驚人
需要更多勁爆的劇本餵養
表演者難免不經意的暴露隱私
窺視者循著蛛絲馬跡找到真相
討賞，變成一樁樁不堪的醜聞

迷戀威士忌的方式

迷戀威士忌
用最單純的方式把瓶塞丟掉
如同買一張單程車票
回不去了，才能盡情享用
毫不保留，才能淋漓暢快
換一種表情，換一種姿勢
換一種心情，換一種態度

深色厚實的瓷器杯子
鎖住威士忌的果香與麥芽香
玻璃水晶的透明杯子
散發威士忌的花香與日光香

The appetite of the peepers is great

More exciting plays are needed to feed it

The performer subconsciously reveal their secret

The peeper finds the truth through some flimsy traces

Asking for favor, is one after another unbearable scandal

The Way of Being Infatuated with Whisky

Being infatuated with whisky

Abandon the cork in the simplest way

Like buying a single ticket

No way back, enjoyment to the heart's content

Without any reserve, and ease of mind

In another expression, in another posture

In another mood, in another attitude

The china cup which is thick and of deep color

Locks the fragrance of fruit and malt of whisky

The transparent cup of glass crystal

Emanating the flowery and sunny fragrance of whisky

聞香，試味，品酒
芬芳在鼻中瀰漫
醇郁在口中迴旋
滿足在心中綻放

不要乾杯
釀酒人的溫柔值得你慢慢回味
不要乾杯
飲酒人才能從容優雅貫穿古今

迷戀威士忌
可以用最單純的方式
也可以試著改變態度

Smelling, sniffing, tasting

Fragrance overflowing in the nose

Sweetness lingering in the mouth

Contentment blossoming in the heart

No clicking cups

The warmth of wine brewer is for your taste and aftertaste

No clicking cups

The wine drinker can be easy and elegant through time of yore

Being infatuated with whisky

The simplest way may be adopted

And the attitude may also be changed

(Translated by Zhang Zhizhong)

許其正詩選

詩人簡介

　　許其正,台灣當代傑出的詩人、作家、翻譯家。臺灣屏東縣人,1939 年生,東吳大學法學士;曾任編輯、記者、軍法官、教師兼部分文學社團負責人、指導教師等;現在已退休。

　　許氏自小對文藝及寫作具有興趣,於 1960 年開始發表作品,以新詩與散文為主,多寫鄉土、田園、大自然,歌頌人生光明面,勉人奮發向上;已出版 26 本著作,其中 14 本為詩集;作品被譯成英文、日文、希臘文、蒙古文、希伯來文、俄文、法文、葡萄牙文與馬爾他文,被選入近百種選集,詩、散文及劇本曾多次得獎,曾獲國際詩歌翻譯研究中心頒發榮譽文學博士學位及 2004 年最佳國際詩人,美國世界文化藝術學院頒發榮譽文學博士,國際作家藝術家協會頒發榮譽人文博士及英譯中最佳翻譯,希

臘札斯特朗文學會頒發紀念獎，黎巴嫩耐吉・阿曼文學獎頒發詩歌榮譽獎，曾被提名為 2014 年度諾貝爾文學獎候選人。

　　他現在專事閱讀與寫作，作品以中、英、日、希臘、蒙古等語文，在國內外報紙、雜誌發表，並兼任《大海洋詩雜誌》&《世界詩人》顧問及《華文現代詩》編委，國際作家藝術家協會會員，希臘札斯特朗文學會榮譽會員。

Selected Poems of Hsu ChiCheng

About the Poet

　　Hsu Chicheng，a distinguished contemporary Taiwanese poet, writer and translator, native of Pingtung County, Taiwan; born in 1939; LLB of Soochow University. He was once an editor, a journalist, a military judge, a teacher as well as part-time director, leading member or guiding teacher to some mass organizations of art and literature. He has now retired.

　　From his childhood, he is fond of literature and writing. Since 1960 he started to publish his works, most of his works are poems and prose, mainly depicting native land, idyllic life and nature, singing the praise of the brilliant side of human experience, based on humanity to encourage people to brace themselves up and be bent on doing good deeds. He has published 26 books including 14 collections of poems. Many of his poems have been translated into English, Japanese, Greek, Mongolian, Hebrew, Russian, French, Portuguese, Maltese and recorded in near hundred selections of poems. His poems, prose works and plays have won prizes for times. He was conferred an honorary doctorate of literature and one of the international best poets 2004 by The International Poetry Translation And Research Centre, was conferred also an honorary doctorate of literature by The U.S. World Academy of Arts and Culture, was conferred also a doctor honoris causa in humanities as well as the best translator from English to Chinese by The International Writers and Artists Association and was presented the commemorative prize by Literary Club "Xasteron", Greece, was presented also the honour prize by Naji Naaman's Literary prizes, Lebanon. Moreover, he was nominated for Nobel Prize in Literature, 2014.

He now specializes in reading and writing. Most of his poems are published in Chinese, English, Greek, Japanese or Mongolian both at home and abroad. He is at present the part-time adviser of *Large Ocean Quarterly & The World Poets Quarterly*, editor of *Chinese Modern Poetry Quarterly*. He is member of International Writers and Artists Association, honorary member of Literature Club "Xasteron", Greece.

山不講話

山不講話
山就是不講話

我從遠處招呼他
他不講話
我走前去親近他
他不講話
我大聲問他
他不講話
我氣得踹了他一下
他還是不講話
我只得失望地離開他
他還是不講話

我偏著頭
想了一下又一下
我終於想通了：
山最偉大！

The Mountain doesn't Speak

The mountain doesn't speak
The mountain still doesn't speak

I beckon him
He doesn't speak
I go near him
He doesn't speak
I loudly ask him
He doesn't speak
I get angry and give a kick at him
He doesn't speak
With disappointment I go away from him
He still doesn't speak

I think of it in doubt
Over and over
I finally find the answer:
The mountain is the greatest

(*Translated by the Poet*)

樹的晨禱

早安，神啊
我是樹
請垂聽我由衷的祈禱：

暗夜已經過去
晨曦已經隱約初現
請太陽趕緊升上來吧
我需要太陽的光來製造氧氣
他們人類正有待於氧氣來救命呢

他們是製造廢氣的族類
在這公園裡運動的他們
用他們的身體製造
從他們的嘴巴、鼻孔、屁股、皮膚
釋放出來
污染大地，污染他們自己
這還不甚嚴重

Morning Prayer of Trees

Good morning, oh, God
I am a tree
Please listen to my heartfelt prayer:

The darkness has passed
Morning rays begin to appear
Please let the sun rise up
I need sunshine to make oxygen
With which to save the lives of human beings

They are the type who make waste gas
While doing exercise in the park
They make it with their body
From their mouths, nostrils, buttocks, and skin
It is released
The earth is polluted, and they themselves are polluted
This is not so serious

在別的地方，或遠或近
有他們經營的工廠
燃燒木材，燃燒油料，燃燒煤炭
從煙囪冒出濃濃的油煙、廢氣
那些更是不得了
除了臭而外
還有各種有毒的氣體
弄得到處烏煙瘴氣
毒害動物、植物，甚至他們自己
讓萬物和他們自己奄奄一息

原諒他們吧！
他們或許不自知
他們或許有他們的苦衷
為了餵飽他們的肚子？
為了賺取更多的財富？
為了擴張自己的勢力？
不必去管那麼多
他們是太可憐了
爭生存，爭權力，爭錢財
不擇手段，無所不為
不顧其他族類，甚至戕害自己

In other places, either near or far

There are factories run by them

To burn timber, fuel, and coal

Heavy lampblack and waste gas from chimneys

Bring more danger

In addition to their unpleasant smell

There are various poisonous gases

Everywhere is a foul atmosphere

To let animals, plants, even themselves poisonously

To drive myriads of beings and themselves to death's door

Please forgive them!

Perhaps they do not know it

Perhaps they have their own worries and troubles

In order to fill their own stomaches?

In order to make more wealth?

In order to strengthen their power?

For all that

They are too piteous

Striving for existence, for power, for wealth

By hook or by crook, doing whatever they think is right

Irrespective of other families, even killing their own kind

原諒他們吧
他們有他們不得已的苦衷
他們所做的他們不知道

可憐可憐他們吧！
請太陽趕快升上來
我需要太陽的光來製造氧氣
他們正有待於那些氧氣來救命呢
雖則他們沒有自覺，不請求
我比他們更急呢！

請垂聽我由衷的祈禱吧！
我是樹
神啊，感謝您！

拾　級

一腳高
一腳低
兩腳輪番地

Please forgive them!

They have their own worries and troubles

They do not know what they are doing

Please take pity on them!

Please let the sun rise up

I need sunshine to make oxygen

With which to save their lives

They lack conscious awareness, and they do not press for it

But I worry more than them!

Please listen to my heartfelt prayer!

I am a tree

Oh God, thank you!

(Translated by Zhang Zhizhong)

Stepping

High is one foot

Low is another foot

Take turns are the two feet

踩踏著梯級
踩踏著梯級
一步就是一步
人便向上昇了

人生旅途，長長久久
有時是有風雨的
或許風強雨又急
有時是有烈陽的
或許烈陽炙人如焚
或許更有坎坷崎嶇
而且前面還有無數梯級

那有什麼好憂懼呢
越多困阻
越要踩穩腳步，向上
以穩健的腳步
粉碎重重困阻
樂觀以對吧！
哈，向上，向上！

踩踏著梯級

Tread on the steps
Tread on the steps
One step is the one step
One is raised

It's long the route of life
Sometimes there are storm
May be strong the wind and at high speed the rain
Sometimes there is raging sun
Maybe scorching as burning
Maybe there are rugged road
And there are numberless steps in front of

Why afraid of it?
The more obstacles
The more we step steadily, upward
Crush the obstacles layer upon layer
With the steady steps
Confront with optimistic
Ha, upward, upward!

Tread on the steps

一步一步向上
風雨、烈陽、坎坷崎嶇這些困阻
於我何有哉？
即使已經汗流浹背
即使已經氣喘吁吁
即使已經黃昏……

夢裡彩虹

常常從這裡走過
只要是有太陽的晴天
在這河廊噴水處 (註)
就著陽光照映水氣
從一定的角度
看向那噴出的濛濛水氣
便不難看到彩虹

那可是一個夢吧！

一個夢？

Upward one step by one step

What to do about

The obstacles of the storm, the raging sun and the rugged road?

Even the streaming with sweat

Even are out of breath

Even the dusk is here

（Translated by the Poet）

Rainbow in the Dream

I often walk over there

Only if it's the sunny day

At the fountain of the passageway of the river*

I always face the steam the sunshine shined upon

From some angle

To view the drizzly steam the fountain sprinkled

And can see the rainbow without difficulty

May it be a dream?

A dream?

夢裡有首詩？
夢裡有個世外？
非黑白，是七彩的
哇！紅橙黃綠藍靛紫
是和平無爭，安和樂利的
所在！

是從那一年起的
我總就著彩虹發想
彩虹裡有一個夢便
每天每時每刻
總是夢著
要去追尋
要去抓取

每每在雨初落時
每每在雨將停未停時
只要是細雨的時候
如果有陽光
有陽光映照水氣的時候
彩虹便出現

Is there a piece of poetry in the dream?

Is there a paradise in the dream?

It's not a black and white, but a colourful

Wow, red, orange, yellow, green, blue, indigo-blue and purple

It's certainly a place of

Peace without struggle, live and work in peace

From that year I started

To face the rainbow I think of

There is a dream in the rainbow

I always dream

To search it

To grab it

Every day every hour every moment

It often in the beginning of the rain

It often in the rain will stop

Just there is the time of fine rain

If there is the sunshine

The sunshine shined the steam

The rainbow will appear

什麼時候可以追尋得到？
什麼時候可以抓住？

日日期盼著
日日夢想著
有時候好像看見了
卻在朦朧裡，在渺茫裡
有時候好像抓住了
雖似唾手可得，卻又距我頗遠
就像現在所在的位子
彩虹就在那些水氣裡
在陽光的映照下
似唾手可得
可是真的唾手可得嗎？

從那一年起，我
費盡心血，汗流浹背
一生夢想，追尋，抓取
總是在朦朧裡，在渺茫裡
總似唾手可得，卻又距離我頗遠
什麼時候什麼地方
可以抓取得到？
可以擁有？

When will I search it out?

When will I grab it out?

I hope every day

I dream every day

It seems I view it some time

But it's obscure, it's vague

It seems I grab it

But it also in the distance though it seems can be easily obtained

It's like I stand in the place now

The rainbow is in the steam

Under the sunshine shined up

It seems can be easily obtained

However, may it really be easily obtained?

From that year

I cudgel all my heart and blood, streaming with sweat

Dreaming, searching and grabbing whole my life

It always obscure, it always vague

It always seems can be easily obtained but in some more distance

When and where

Can I grab it?

Can I possess it?

啊，信誓吧！
一定要追尋得到！
一定要抓取得到！
一定要擁有！

　　註：河廊，係指新莊中港河廊。該河廊原為中港
大排，乃一大排水溝，吸納各家戶廢水，髒污不堪；
後新北市水利局予以整治，於 2012 年初開放，使兼
具排水與休閒功能。平日只要天氣不差，時間許可，
我便在下午四點左右，走這條河廊到思賢公園做運
動，邊走邊欣賞其美景。其中有好幾處有噴水設施。
我每每到噴水處時便停步觀賞，作平生一直以來的
夢。很妙的是，往新北大道方向看去，在近中原路處，
設計者造了一個人工彩虹。雖非真正的彩虹，遠遠望
去，卻疑似真彩虹。本詩乃觀賞之所得。

Oh, I pledge

Surely, I must search it!

Surely, I must grab it!

Surely, I must possess it!

    * The passageway of the river refers to the passageway of the river of Hsin-Chuang. Originally, it's the grand drainer that accepts whole the waste water of the families, dirty and filthy, then repaired by The Water Conservancy Bureau of New Taipei City and open to the public in the beginning of 2012, let it has the function both of drain and leisure. Only the weather is fine generally, and it permits of time, I'll walk to Si Xian Park from this passageway for exercise at about 4 PM in the afternoon precise the beautiful scene as well as walking. There are many places of fountain by the way. Every time I walk near the fountain I will stop and appreciate it and work of my dream. It's very wonderful that there is an artificial rainbow when I look forward to Hsinpei Blvd near Chung Yuan Road. It's very like the rainbow look from distance though it's not the true. The poem is obtained from appreciation.

（Translated by the Poet）

梅花的畫像

從1939年迢迢而來
經過千山萬水
忍受風霜雨雪
不畏崎嶇坎坷
我來到角板山上
和梅花一起照相

我站在梅花前方
兩相緊緊靠近
一按照相機按鈕
梅花便紛紛
把我的頭髮染成了
一片白　一片
堅定不屈　一片
崢嶸的山巒

Plum's Portrait

Far from 1939

Through millions of mountains and rivers

Borne countless of wind and rain, snow and frost

No afraid of vicissitude of ruggedness

I come to the plum garden of Jiaopan Shan

To take a photograph with the plum

I stand in front of a plum

So closely we near together

As press the button of the camera

The petals of the plum

Dyed my hairs into

A stretch of white, a stretch of

Firmness, and a stretch of

Lofty and steel mountains

(Translated by the Poet)

莫渝詩選

詩人簡介

　　莫渝，本名林良雅，1948年出生，臺灣苗栗竹南人。淡江大學畢業。目前負責《笠》詩刊主編（2005 年 8 月起）。長期與詩文學為伍，閱讀世界文學，關心台灣文學。翻譯：《法國古詩選、19 世紀、20 世紀詩選》三冊、《惡之華》、《比利提斯之歌》等。近年出版詩集：《第一道曙光》（2007）、《革命軍》（2010）、《走入春雨》（2011）、台語  詩集《春天 ê 百合》（2011）、《光之穹頂》等。評論集《台灣詩人群像》（2007）、《波光瀲灩 —— 20 世紀法國文學》（2007）、《台灣詩走影》等。編詩文集《詩人愛情社會學》

（2011）、《笠園玫瑰 ── 笠女詩人選集》（2012）等。詩作曾譯為英、日、韓、德、蒙古、土耳其文等。

Selected Poems of Mo Yu

About the Poet

Mo Yu（b.1948） is pen name of Lin Liang-ya, graduated from Taichung Normal College and the French Department of Tamkang University. Mo Yu started writing and published poetry in 1964. Mo Yu has published his poetic work：Wordless Spring（1979）, Love Song of The Earth（1986）, Clouds（1990）,The Mirror of The Water（1998）,Poems Mo Yu 一（2005）,Poems Mo Yu 二（2005）,The First Aurora（2007）,Going the Spring Rain（2011）.He also published his poetic work

Taiwannese：Lilies in Spring（2011），Light of Sky（2013）
On the other hand, he is a translator of French poetry, and a commentator.

走入春雨

追逐東北季風的行蹤
趕赴一場極品祭典
我們的腳泥濘在春雨的濡潤中

雨，柔細地拍拂
沾衣不濕
斜風，停靠耳根喃喃

雨，輕飄飄地拍拂
把軟綿綿的溫沁
鋪蓋地面
還深情地植入土壤
發出悄聲
一定要拉牢眾人的腳

留住春雨
春雨
沉澱我們的囂嚷
溶蝕我們身上的塵埃
一起淨化家鄉

Enter Spring Rain

Pursue the trace of northeast monsoon
Go for a grand sacrifice ceremony
Our feet are muddy in the spring rain

Raindrops, softly beat
To moisten the clothes
A slant wind, murmuring into ears

Raindrop, gently beat
To spread the soft warmth
All over the ground
While affectionately planting it into the soil
Giving a quiet voice
Be sure to hold fast the feet of the crowd

Keep spring rain
Spring rain
Sediments our noises
To wash away the dust on us
Together to clean our hometown

挖　掘

整地。在菜園裡
用鋤頭用鐵鍬盡力耕鋤，掘土挖深
清除地表作物，收割與挫敗的作物
請他們回到地層下
騰出廣大空間
從無求取真有的實相

用鐵鍬挖地　深深地挖
用力翻出地底的土　深埋的黑土
翻出夾帶嫩根細鬚的土塊
翻出沒被陽光曬過的暗色土壤
讓地心反轉

已經被作物汲取營養的表土
辛苦過了
一律請回地底休息
輪換陰涼潤軟的底土跟太陽招呼

Digging

The whole land. In the vegetable garden
To dig with a hoe or a spade, to dig deep into the soil
Get rid of ground surface crops, harvest crops
For them to enter beneath the earth
To make more space
The truth of seeking real from nothing

Dig with a spade　deep into the earth
The soil upturned with force　the deep buried black soil
Upturned is the soil block with fine roots and hairs
Upturned is the dark soil which has not been sunned
For the earth's core to be reversed

The surface soil where nutrition has been absorbed by crops
Efforts have been made
Please rest back to the ground
The bottom soil which takes turns for the shade salutes the sun

用力挖深，挖掘
祖先活動過的痕跡
揣想他們的智慧
挖深　再深　更深

翻土
從黑暗的地底
覓尋新生的景色和氣象

風林火山

——給 65 歲的自己

風

勁疾猛襲不再
彷彿淨身靈修後的柔軟身段
減緩凜然
徐徐地吹拂，薰風

即使靜止

Dig forcefully, dig

In search of the living trace of our ancestors

Guess their wisdom

Dig deep　　deep　　deep

Turn the soil

From the dark ground

In search of the newborn view and atmosphere

Wind Forest Volcano

－ To myself at 65

The Wind

No more fierce and attacking

Like the soft limbs after spiritual practice through body cleaning

Stern is reduced

Blow slowly, warm wind

Even if quiet

聆聽所有的聲籟
轉運成氣　增進耳清目明

來自海上夾帶濕鹹水份的西南季風
輕輕吹向我們摯愛的土地
吹拂珍惜的人間

林

因為清風，林梢
微微擺盪
傳知生命必然的活
動

不只一棵　兩棵
既縱深的黝黑暗鬱
也橫廣的高聳挺拔

引人遐思的樹林有一處可憩的空地
可懷的人家

To listen to all noises

Turn the luck into air   enhance sharp eyes and quick ears

The southwest monsoon from the sea which is moist and salty

Gently blows toward our beloved great earth

Blowing in the cherished world

The Forest

Owing to a breeze, the treetops

Are gently waving

Telling the activity of a necessary

Life

Not only one   or two trees

Both deeply dark and melancholy

And widely high and towering

A vacant plot in the trees which are thought-provoking

Nostalgic households

火

曾經兇悍燎原的火勢已經褪弱
喪失侵掠吞噬的本質

仍然需要燃燒

持續添些柴薪
維繫火苗　穩定火候

讓自己保暖　讓周圍感受溫馨

山

山不動
依然有夢　孕育
有愛　蘊藏

墨綠翠鬱的植被　土黃堅實的底質
千百年　億萬年
不言說　不表明
靜靜囤積能量

The Fire

The ever ferocious fire has faded
And has lost its nature of devour and plunder

Still in need of burning

Keep adding firewood
To nurse the flame　maintain the fire

Keep myself warm　for the environment to be warm

The Mountain

The mountain remains still
Still the dream　to gestate
With love　contained in it

The lushly emerald vegetation　the texture of hard yellow soil
Thousands of years　millions of years
No words　no airing of opinions
Silently store up energy

靜靜滋生草木吸引動物奔逐

山不動
巍巍屹立，等你靠近

不動的山
等你來移轉

軌道的記憶

——記「淡水文化園區」及其前身「殼牌倉庫」

一小截雙軌鐵道
鋪陳歷史的片簡影像
河道港口風光歲月的興衰

首先
敗戰的清廷開放淡水為通商口岸
啓動船影林立風帆揚舞新紀元
岸邊洋行比鄰，商賈走動
忙迭於出口台灣茶葉、煤、樟腦等

Quietly nurture grass and coax animals to run and chase

The mountain is silent
Standing and towering　　for you to approach

The immobile mountain
Waits for you to move

The Memory of Rails

— On "Tamsui Culture Park" and Its Precedent "Shell Warehouse"

A small section of double-track railway
Paves the brief image of history
The vicissitudes of riverside years

First of all
The defeated Qing Dynasty Government open the Tamsui as
　　trading ports
To start the new age thick with ships and sails
Along the banks foreign firms throng, businessmen going
　　about in a hurry
Busy about exporting Taiwan tea, coal, and camphor

英商跟上設立嘉士洋行，在鼻仔頭
亞細亞火油子公司 Rising Sun 迺生產隨後介入
1897 年，英國 Shell 殼牌運輸貿易公司進駐取代
擴建倉庫，掌控燃油動能
鋪設軌道，聯通縱貫鐵路支線淡水線
方便油品輸送

謀取更大利潤的繁榮
即使石油槽煤油槽的濃臭味
惹來私語「臭油棧」倉庫的嫌憎
繁榮繼續繁華

戰爭末期
美軍空襲北台灣
1944 年轟炸油庫，頓然煙消灰滅
英商一蹶不振

秋日午後
在鼻仔頭咖啡 Piatow Coffee 歇歇
瀏覽園區百年磚砌古建築
老樹添加暮涼

British businessmen follow up by establishing firms, in Piatow
The Asian Company of Rising Sun is involved after production
In 1897, British Shell Transport and Trading Company replaces
Expanding the warehouse, control kinetic energy of fuel oil and
　　expand warehouse
Lay tracks, connect branches railway lines
Convenient for the transportation of oil and food

Prosperity of seeking more profit
In spite of the heavy odor of oil tanks and kerosene tanks
Soliciting hate from private words "smelly oil stack"
Prosperity continues

At the end of war
American army air attacks the north of Taiwan
In 1944 to bomb oil depots, a sudden reduction to ashes
The British businessmen cannot recover after a setback

In the afternoon of an autumn
Rest at Piatow Coffee
Visiting the century-old brick building in the park
Dusk cool veils the old trees

接軌的故事不會中斷
新世紀用隱形軌道
聯繫外城
和世界緊密握手

Continuous stories never stop

With invisible tracks the new century

Connects the outside city

Tightly shake hands with the world

曾美霞詩選

詩人簡介

女，1950 年生於臺灣高雄

學歷：臺北市立大學中文研究所碩士。

經歷：曾任中華民國新詩學會理事及副秘書長，《中國詩刊》主編。

現任：中國文藝協會秘書長《文學人》編輯召集人，《華文現代詩》副總編輯。

作品：詩集《山動了》。散文集《波女與息女》。短篇小說集《出軌》，《消失的紫》。長篇小說《翩翩飛翔》。電視劇本《紅娘》系列。

Selected Poems of Tzeng Meihsia

About the Poet

Female, born in 1950 in Kaohsiung, Taiwan Education background: Master's degree from the Chinese Research Institution of Taipei Municipal University.Experience: She has been a council member and deputy secretary general of New Poetry Society of Republic of China, as well as editor-in-chief of *China Poetry*.Currently she is secretary general of China Literature & Art Association, editing convener of *Literary Men*, and vice editor-in-chief of *Chinese Modern Poetry Quarterly*.Her works: Poetry collection *The Mountain Has Been Moved*.Prose collection *The Billow Maiden and Silent Maiden*.Collection of short stories *Derailment* and *The Disappearing Purple Color*.A novel entitled *Soaring and Flying*.Telescript series *The Matchmaker*.

詩偷走人的感情

為一首詩歌悸動
不是年少的心靈脆弱
被一行詩句吸引
不是青春年華太多憧憬
只因為詩,總是偷走人的感情

詩,並不限定愛情的結局
但往往設下陷阱
無論是喜劇收場還是悲劇重演
詩,一律歌頌愛情
教人嚮往愛情

Poetry Has Stolen a Person's Emotion

Moved by a poem
Not owing to the juvenile weak mind
Attracted by a line of poetry
Not that youthful years are full of yearnings
Only because poetry, always steals a person's emotion away

Poetry, does not limit itself to the ending of love
But it never fails to set a trap
Whether ending by comedy or repeated tragedy
Poetry, constantly eulogizes love
Teaches people to yearn for love

詩，將人生的精華化為一格畫面
或是一把鑰匙，一串密碼
不知道哪一首詩，會在哪一個時間
開啓哪一個封閉的心靈
讓希望的光照射進來

當時光飛逝，從前已經過去
仇恨與醜陋，逐漸褪色脫落
一切的美好依然停留在詩中
曾經吟誦的草地陽光，雨滴雲朵
彷彿從來不曾離開

人生，脫不開歲月的關照
自己能掌握的其實不多
除了詩

風鈴的呢喃

鈴緘默，享受午後慵懶的自在
風任性，恣意攪亂這片刻的寧靜

Poetry, frames the cream of life into a picture
Or a key, or a series of codes
Not knowing which poem, in which period of time
To open which enclosed soul
For the light of hope to penetrate

When time flies, former times have past
Hate and ugliness, gradually fade and peel off
All beauty still exists in poetry
The sunny lawn and raindrops and cloudy blossoms ever sung
As if have never been away from us

Life, cannot dispense with the cares of years
Actually we cannot grasp many
Except poetry

Whispers of the Windbell

Silent is the windbell, enjoying the lethargic and easeful afternoon
The wind is wanton, to disturb the momentary quietness

風，吹打著鈴
鈴，立刻叮叮噹噹響起來
如同信差發佈了訊息

聒噪不是鈴的本意，是唯一出路
鈴只是風存在的註解
風卻是鈴存在的必要

無風的鈴
孤單的懸在屋簷下的窗口
獨自追尋夜空中掠過天際的流星
獨自落寞，獨自幸福

風中的鈴
搖晃著刻畫歲月飛逝的軌跡
獨自捕捉午後一朵沒有雨的雲
獨自心酸，獨自渴望

懸浮在不見天不著地的半空
陣陣春風吻過，年年秋風拂過
當殘夢初醒，蔓延開來的
是無止境的茫然

The wind, blows the bell
And the bell, instantly rings
As if a messenger is sending a message

Noise is not the intention of the bell, it is the only way out
The bell is the footnote of the wind
And the wind is the necessity of the bell

The windless bell
Solitarily hangs above the window under the eaves
Solitarily pursuing the shooting stars flitting across the night sky
Solitarily melancholy, solitarily happy

The bell in the wind
Is shaking the carving trace of flying years
Solitarily capture a blossom of cloud without rain in the
        afternoon
Solitarily sad, solitarily yearning

Floating in the mid-air far from the sky and the earth
Spells after spells of spring wind past, year after year autumn
        wind blows
When awake from a remnant dream, what is spreading
Is the boundless blankness

存在主義電話亭

我的存在不是主義
只是需要
我之所以是我現在這個樣子
是因為我的重要與獨特
我思故我在

我被淘汰不是罪過
只是潮流
面臨拆除的痛苦
存在主義強調
必須尋求存在的意義
才能延續另一種存在

尼采之後
技術統治了世界，製造了一切
人的人性，物的物性
都是市場上可以算計的價值

The Telephone Booth of Existentialism

My existence is not –ism
Only a kind of need
I become what I am now
Owing to my importance and uniqueness
I think, there I am

It is not a shame for my being obsoleted
It is only a trend
Facing the pain of being torn down
Emphasis of the existentialism
We must seek the meaning of existence
So as to continue another existence

After Nietzsche
Technology has controlled the world, and has manufactured
    everything
Humanity of people, animality of animals
All become the value to be counted on the market

苦難是具有意義的
飛鳥射盡了，就收起弓箭
兔子捕盡了，就烹煮獵狗
一切看起來多麼合理
涼爽的秋天一到
扇子顯得如此多餘

如果街頭巷口容不下我
存在，失去意義
不如優雅轉身下台
歸去

街頭郵筒

儘管全身漆上草原樹木的綠
展現出親切自然
也是徒勞
誰在乎呢

Hardships are meaningful

When all flying birds have been shot, the bow is disused

When all rabbits have been captured, the hound is cooked

All seems to be reasonable

With the advent the cool autumn

The fans are worthless

If the streets and lanes fail to contain me

Existence, loses its meaning

Better step down from the stage elegantly

And return

Street Mailbox

It is vain for you to be thoroughly painted

With the green of grassland trees

Exhibiting natural familiarity

Who cares

一整個火焰色標記了你曾經紅過
那又怎樣
落伍的就該退場
限時專送算什麼
即時通訊才是王道

虛擬科技的空襲洗劫
八百里加急早已人仰馬翻
飛鴿傳書只是遠古的神話
一張郵票所承載的浪漫不見了
彼此深濃的牽掛與期盼失落了

有事，立刻語音對話
不方便說的，傳送文字
想表達情緒，隨手抓個貼圖
競速世代
不是 e 什麼，就是 i 什麼
還有誰會把喜怒哀樂丟進郵筒

沒人寄信了
連賀年卡也被遺忘了
偶爾收到幾份廣告傳單

The whole flame has marked you for your ever been popular
And so what
He who falls back should bow out
Special delivery within time limit is nothing
Better than it is the actual communication

The air raid and sack of virtual science
Urgent for eight hundred li suffers a crushing defeat
Flying pigeons as carriers of letters are remote myth
The romance carried by a post stamp is nowhere to be seen
The mutual heavy solicitude and expectation is lost

In urgent case, instant voice conversation
If inconvenient, words sending
To express emotions, a casual chartlet
The age of speed competition
Whatever e, or whatever i
Who will throw their joys and sorrows into the mailbox

Nobody sends a letter
Even New Year cards have been forgotten
Occasionally a few flyers are received

彩色油墨刺眼而生冷無味
本地外埠兩張口依舊終日飢渴
空蕩蕩的肚子盡是苦澀

雖然紅綠郵筒總是並列相伴
卻在街頭各自孤單

貓等待

貓等待，當牠喝不到牛奶
貓等待有人打開瓶蓋
好舔那牛奶

我等待，當我得不到我的愛
我等待有人被淘汰
好親近我的愛

貓忍耐，若牠得不到關懷
貓忍耐主人的不睬
直到主人發現牠的乖

The colorful printing inks are glaringly insipid
The two mouths of local and other cities are still thirsty day
　　after day
In the empty stomach nothing but bitterness

Though red and green mailboxes always stand side by side
They are respectively lonely in the street

The Cat Is Waiting

The cat is waiting, when he fails to drink the milk
The cat is waiting for somebody to open the lid
To suck the milk

I am waiting, when I fail to receive my love
I wait for somebody to be eliminated
So as to be close to my love

The cat endures, if he fails to be cared
The cat endures the ignorance of his master
Until the master finds his docility

我忍耐，若我得不到青睞
我忍耐愛人的責怪
直到愛人明白我的深情如海

貓以優雅睿智的自在
等待時間的空白
我以年華老去的慷慨
等待生命的
再一次澎湃

春天隨想之一

春雨未歇　最適合幻想
不被打擾是私密的幸福
去年做的夢輕輕的飄浮反芻
再次咀嚼複習陶醉的滋味
樹梢的新芽嫩嫩的綠出油來

我和我，在日記中爭辯
我和我，在現實中妥協

I endure, if I fail to be loved
I endure my love's blame
Until my love understands my deep emotion like a sea

With its ease and elegance the cat
Is waiting for the blankness of time
With the generosity of aging years
I wait for my life
To surge and swell again

Random Thought of Spring (1)

Spring rain does not let up　suitable for fantasy
Not to be disturbed means private happiness
The dream of last year gently wafts and ruminates
Again chew and brush up the flavor of intoxication
The new buds on treetops are tenderly green

I and myself, are debating in a diary
I and myself, come to terms in reality

隱藏慾望是人類的擅長與專利
刻意製造浪漫的邂逅
卻瀟灑的假裝不在乎

有些慾望，隱藏了就淡薄了
有些慾望，日久了就昇華了
單戀或許會結束
思念絕不會停止

未完待續只是春雨中的幻想
分手殺青卻是早已畫下的句點

春天隨想之二

當你靠近
我知道你帶來的不只是陽光的燦爛
而是更多美麗的色彩
還有讓人悸動的慈悲

億萬千年以前的一粒沙

Concealing desires is human advantage and patent

Intently to have a romantic encounter

Yet pretending to be smart and careless

Some desires, become lessened when concealed

Some desires, are sublimated with growing days

An unrequited love may come to an end

But the missing never ends

To be continued is the fantasy of spring rain

The break-up final editing has already been the full stop
under the pen

Random Thought of Spring (2)

When you approach

I know what you bring here is not only the bright sunshine

But more brilliant colors

And the touching benevolence

A grain of sand millions of year ago

如今是否仍在塵世翻滾
斜陽下的一抹夕照
是否捎來親切的問候

不能總是把影子當玩伴
孤獨的人祈求，施捨一個眼神

旅途有沒有盡頭
流浪者尋找，一個棲息地

追逐，再追逐
等待，再等待
誰能告訴我，漫長的追逐與等待之後
是否有獎賞

春天，在溫暖的午後回答
沈重不該是季節的起點

Is it still rolling in the mortal world
A beam of slanting sun
Does it bring endearing greeting

We cannot always regard our shadows as playmates
The lonely people pray, to be given in charity a look

Is there an end to our journey
The wanderers look for, a habitat

Pursue, again pursue
Wait, again wait
Who can tell me, after long pursuing and waiting
Is there a reward

Spring, the answer in the warm afternoon
Heaviness is not the starting point of the season

陳福成詩選

詩人簡介

陳福成，祖籍四川成都，1952年生於台中。筆名：古晟、藍天、司馬千；法名：本肇居士。

學歷：陸官 44 期、三軍大學82 年班、復興崗政研所畢業、清華大學高科技管理班、政治大學社會科學研究方法班結業。

經歷：野戰部隊各職、政大民族系所講座、台灣大學主任教官、志工、復興電台主講、國安會助理研究員、華夏春秋　雜誌社社長、出版社主編。

思想：以「黃埔人」為職志，以「生長在台灣的中國人」為榮。創作、寫詩，鑽研「中國學」，以貢獻所能和所學為自我實現途徑，以宣揚春秋大義為一生志業。

著作：包含國防、軍事、戰略、兵法、兩岸關係、領導管理、小說、翻譯、現代詩、大學和高中職學校教科書及人生小品數十種。

現職：空大兼任講師、中國詩歌藝術學會理事與常務理事、中國文藝協會理事與員、中華民國新詩學會會員，台大逸仙學會、登山會與教授聯誼會會員、台大校園志工、遠望雜誌社委、葡萄園詩刊同仁、佛光山台北教師分會會員、中華戰略學會會員、軍校校友會會員、自由作家、兵法講座。華文現代詩季刊編輯同仁、前台灣大學退聯會理事長。

Selected Poems of Chen Fucheng

About the Poet

Chen Fucheng, a native of Chengdu, Sichuan Province. He was born in 1952 in Taizhong of Taiwan. He has military experiences at several military universities as well as educational experiences at Tsinghua University and Political University. And he has rich experiences in working at different places, such as in the army and at Taiwan University, a researcher, and lectures at radio station, editor-in-chief of a magazine and chief editor of a publishing house, etc. He aims to write poetry and do research in the study of Chinese, to carry forward the cream of Chinese thought. He has published widely, concerning national defense, military affairs and strategy, relationship across the Taiwan Straits, leaderships and management, novels, translation, modern poetry, middle school and university textbooks, as well as philosophy of life, etc. Now he is a part-time university lecturer, councilman of the Association of the Art of Chinese Poetry, a member of the New Chinese Poetry Association, etc.

外公外婆刀劍錄

外公雖有點年紀
武功還在　他善於用劍
往昔劍不虛發　見血封喉
叫誰閉嘴誰就閉嘴
要擺平誰就必能擺平誰
只是他現在早已沒有用劍的對象了
連練劍的對象也沒有
他已經按耐不住
氣憋著不發會重傷筋脈
這天他決心乘兒女們回來好好出劍
回憶他們往昔的刀劍傳奇
奇俠夫妻如何主持武林正義
懷念他們位高權重能呼風喚雨
武林中一片祥和　俠者仁心
社會上一片和諧　人存友愛
家族中長幼有序　重視倫理
如今
一切都顛覆了
一切都崩盤了

Fighting Between My Grandparents

Old is my maternal grandfather
His martial arts are still with him　he is good at sword
In his youth he is accurate and sharp with his sword
All would yield to the power of his sword
All bow to him owing to his sword
But now he has no object for his sword
Even no object for the exercise of his sword
He is impatient
He will be mortally wounded if smothers and never lets it out
Today he is determined to show his sword when his children are
　　back home
To recall their memory of legend of sword
How the chivalrous couple would carry justice in the circle of
　　martial arts
Missing them for their high place, prestige, and capabilities
In the circle of martial arts harmony reigns　chivalrous people
　　are with a benevolent heart
The society is all harmony　and people are friendly
In the family there is precedence of elders　ethics are emphasized
And now
All is overthrown
All collapses

江湖無道　武林無義
俠魔不分　陰陽無別
黑白兩道都無道
外公和外婆不忍再想下去
也不敢再回憶
當江湖只剩下一張床
只是她現在忍一忍　收刀好久了
也因為大家都躲得遠遠的
她也耐不住性子
決心再次出刀
這天乘兒女都回來了
她抓住一個不爽的機會瞬間出刀
不料雪亮的刀飄然才一飛出
竟被一種現代很邪門的武功氣勢逼回
刀尖竟回頭指向外婆的心臟
幸好外婆功夫底子仍有
千鈞一髮間往旁邊一閃
免死
但也氣得血壓上升中風臥床

現在外公外婆只能躺在床上回憶
當武林只剩下一口氣
那刀和劍
就放下吧

Chivalry is no more favored in the circle of martial arts
No distinction of chivalry and demons　of yin and yang
No chivalry in the white world and the dark world
My maternal grandparents can not bear to ponder over it
And they can not bear to recall it
When only one bed is left in the circle of martial arts
Only she has to bear it　the knife has been withdrawn for long
And people keep aloof from it
She can not help to lose her temper
Determined to show the sword again
Today when her children are all back
She takes an unhappy chance to show the knife all of a
　　sudden
Unexpectedly at the flaunt of the snow-white knife
It is overwhelmed by an unexpected modern martial arts
The blade is pointed toward the heart of my maternal
　　grandmother
Luck has it that she still has good martial arts
In the nick of time she dodges to a side
And escapes from death
But she is angered into high blood pressure and bedbound

Now my maternal grandparents can only recall while lying in bed
When the circle of martial arts comes to its last breath
Just put the knife
And sword down

島

微風說起他童年的故事
一排頑皮的樹都哈哈大笑
若得小島唱山歌
山坡上的小草學著村姑的秀髮飄動
陣地旁的士兵鐮刀整修他的散兵坑
春天呵
在我新陳代謝的旺季裏
不要慢了腳步

當鐵扇公主在我上面煽起大火
還得忍受海水燜燉
老樹也要發昏
村落的雞和狗躲起來打盹
祇有打野外的士兵在我身上翻滾
夏天呵
有種把太陽也請下來
這裏是決戰的沙場

The Island

The breeze talks about its childhood
A line of naughty trees are merrily laughing
And the small island is singing a mountain song
The grass on the mountain slope is wafting like the fair hair of
the village girl
The soldiers on the battlefield are repairing the trench with
knives
Oh spring
In my lush season of metabolism
Do not slow down your steps

When the Fan Princess fans a big fire on me
I have to bear the toasting of sea water
The old tree is also dazed
Chickens and dogs are dozing while hiding themselves
Only the outfield soldiers are rolling on me
Oh summer
If you have guts just invite the sun down
This is the battlefield for the final battle

野菊為我披一件高貴的金黃
夕陽忍不住要摹倣
那天邊歸鷹
翱翔的雙翅是我楓葉的箋
此外是戰士荷槍無語對晚風
秋天呵
山後煙囪挺立
把天空潑成一幅畫

漁夫在大海裏佈下陷阱
騙得黃魚螃蟹走錯地方
強風天天打我鬍子的歪主意
雨水常常把我泡的感冒傷風
哨兵更在濃霧中提心吊膽
冬天呵
能夠一年四季永不動搖的
就是我

Wild chrysanthemums put a coat of noble gold on me

The setting sun cannot refrain from imitating

The returning eagle in the horizon

The soaring wings are my letters of maple leaves

Beyond is the soldier with a rifle wordless in the evening

breeze

Oh autumn

Behind the mountain a forest of chimneys stand

To besmear the sky into a painting

The fisherman sets a trap in the sea

Misleading for fishes and crabs to go astray

The gale harbors an evil intention for my beard

The rainwater often drowns me into a cold

The sentinel worries a lot in the heavy fog

Oh winter

Only I can remain motionless through four seasons

Of the year

烽火連三月

從三月十九日點燃一把火
一把假的火
就真的燒了起來
真的燒了四月
真的燒了五月
真的燒了六月

一把一把又一把假的烽火連天的燒
有些在夜裡燜燒
有些就在大白天燎原
有些被嚴密管控在鍋爐中熬燒

瘋火連三月，焚燬了些甚麼？
人證燒了
物證燒了
關鍵影子燒了，關鍵聲音也燒了

The Beacon Fire Burns for Months

To enkindle a fire from March 19
A false fire
And it really burns
Really burns April
Really burns May
Really burns June

A handful after another handful of false beacon fire burns the
sky
Some smoldering in the night
Some burns wildly in the day
Some are strictly kept to be burning in the boiler

Crazy fire for months, what has been burned?
Witness has been burned
Physical evidence has been burned
Key film has been burned, and key voice has been burned

一切不利的因素，全都一把火，一把火……
再一把火，燒個精光

現在，把原來
一座綠油油，水噹噹的
藍天、白雲全都燒了
所有人倫、道德、愛心、信心也燒了
燒成一堆堆
深綠色的灰燼

最後，都燒的差不多了
扁——柏
啟動調查機制
調查那瘋火連三月
瘋火燒了些甚麼？
各有關單位，雷厲風行
針對一堆堆的灰燼
提出一疊疊的報告
總結論：
高溫燒過的灰燼，DNA 不能辨識

All unfavorable factors, all burned by a fire, a handful of fire...
Again a handful of fire, burns everything

Now, the originally green and watery
Blue sky, white clouds
All have been burned
All ethics, morality, loving heart, confidence have also been
burned
Into a pile after another pile
Of dark green ashes

Eventually, almost everything has been burned
Flat —— fir
Investigation has been started
Into the fire burning for months
What has been burned by the crazy fire?
The relevant units are not hesitant to take action
Against a pile after another pile of ashes
A pile after another pile of reports have been raised
Conclusion:
The ashes from high temperature, even DNA fails to recognize

守著一抹藍天

大地被來勢洶洶的綠色泡沫所淹沒
風聲變綠
訊息變綠
影像變綠
原野山谷大地將淹沒在綠色泡沫中
我仍守著一抹藍天

叢林已經綠化了
滿山遍野，凡是能夠紅的發紫都是綠色泡沫
鼠輩走狗當然是深綠色的
成群牛羊搶著吃綠草
犬豬猢猻也人模人樣的披上
綠衣
我仍守著一抹藍天

不管天長地久、海枯石爛
我仍守著一抹藍天
自盤古開天以來
舜日堯天周禮樂

Keeping a Patch of Blue Sky

The great earth has been drowned by the surging green foam
The wind turns green
The message turns green
The image turns green
The wilderness and valley and the earth will be drowned in
green foam
And I am still keeping a patch of blue sky

The woods have been green
All over the mountain, all that can be red is green foam
The mice and running dogs are of course dark green
Herds of cattle and sheep are competing to eat green grass
Even dogs and pigs and monkeys are like human beings
In green coats
I am still keeping a patch of blue sky

In spite of everlasting sky and earth, until the sea is dry and the
rock rusty
I am still keeping a patch of blue sky
Since Pan Gu opens up the sky in ancient time
The ancient sun and sky and the rituality

孔仁孟義漢文章
天就是藍的
有史以來，天都是藍的

逛夜市

各位看倌，我的「公投制憲」
是一種新品牌自發性增高機
不管人家怎麼矮化我們
只要用一次就能高到出頭天

各位看倌，我的「萬能族群溶合劑」
用一瓶就能忘了割喉之痛
讓各大小族群溶合起來
團結在我下面

各位看倌，我的「四不一沒有」都沒有
其實那是一種隱形軟腳劑
別說解放軍，就是十三億
也要叫他通通「春一支嘴」（台語發音）

As well as articles and doctrines of Confucius and Mencius
The sky is blue
Since there is a record of history, the sky is blue

Touring the Night Market

Dear readers, my "public constitution"
Is an automatic heightener of a new brand
No matter how we are shortened by them
Only used once and can be heightened into the sky

Dear readers, my "all-mighty insolvent"
With a bottle of it and the pain of throat cutting is forgotten
For large and small groups to be fused
United under me

Dear readers, there is no "four no one without"
Actually it is an invisible feet softener
Let alone the PLA men, even if 1.3 billion
He will be invariably "a spring mouth"

各位看倌，把上面三藥調成一帖
可以製成「甜心走狗丹」
普天下的人，只要兩天三餐服用
遲早要來朝貢，讓我摸頭

Dear readers, the above three medicines into one
Made into "sweet heart running dog pill"
People under heaven, so long as they take it three meals in
　　two days
Sooner or later to pay tribute, for me to touch the head

陳寧貴詩選

詩人簡介

陳寧貴（ 1954 年 1 月生
－），台灣屏東竹田人（台灣
南部客家聚落六堆的中堆），
曾任出版公司雜誌社社長、總
編輯等職、新詩學會監事、世
界華文詩人協會創會理事。70
年代開始新詩的創作，讀高中
時即加入當時最年輕新銳詩
刊「主流詩社」(1971)、後來
陸續加入「陽光小集詩社」
(1982)、「詩象詩社」(1991)）、

「華文現代詩社」（2014）等，成為推動社務詩運的重要同仁，
並於 2007 年受台灣客家委員會之邀為諮詢委員。創作逾四十
年，近二十年同時使用華語與客語創作。陳寧貴著有詩集「商

怨」暨散文集「天涯與故鄉」等十餘冊。編有「當代新詩大展」
三大冊、「當代散文大展」兩大冊、「世界文學名著的情與慾」
兩冊。作品曾入選現代文學大系、年度台灣詩選、年度散文選。
曾獲教育部詩獎、優秀青年詩人獎、聯合報散文獎等。

Selected Poems of Chen Ninggui

About the Poet

Chen Ninggui, born in January, 1954, is a native of Zhutian
of Pingdong, Taiwan, and he has ever been president of a
publishing house, the editor-in-chief of a magazine, president of
New Poetry Society, and the founding president of the World
Chinese Poets Association. He began writing new poetry in the
70s of the 20th century, and he joined the "Mainstream Poetry
Society" in his senior middle school period (1971), later he
successively joined the "Sunshine Poetry Society" (1982), "Poetry
like poetry society" (1991), and "Chinese Modern Poetry Society"
(2014), etc., and he became an important member to promote the

art of poetry, and in 2007 he was invited to be a member of the advisory committee. He has written for over 40 years, and in the recent 20 years he has been writing in both Chinese and his native language. Chen has published over ten books, including a poetry collection entitled *Commercial Complaint* and collection of prose entitled *The Horizon and Hometown*. In addition, he has compiled three volumes of *Contemporary New Poems*, two volumes of *Contemporary Prose*, and two volumes of *The Emotion and Desire of World Literary Masterpieces*. His works have been included into modern literary series, annual Taiwan poetry selection, and annual prose selection, etc. He has ever won Poetry Prize by the National Education Bureau, Prize for Excellent Young Poets, and Prose Prize for the United Newspapers, etc.

空酒瓶

1

茶几上一只空酒瓶
站立著，像用一條腿撐起體重
沉思的鷺鷥

鷺鷥沒有想飛的樣子
牠似乎依然陶醉在某種芬芳裡
但是，這只酒瓶的確是空的

無可否認，一場大醉過去了
酒的芬芳再也不能吞食我的名字
喝剩的，僅僅是茫茫然
徘徊在空酒瓶裡的
我

The Empty Bottle

1

On the tea table an empty bottle
Is standing, as if it were supporting itself with one leg
The meditating egret

The egret has no intention to fly away
It seems to be intoxicated in some scent
But, the bottle is really empty

There is no denial, the drunkenness has been past
The scent of liquor can no more swallow my name
The leftovers are only blankness
I am loitering in the empty
Bottle

2

深夜，空酒瓶呼喊著渴
張開口，仰著頭
便打起呵欠來

把它握在手中
突然爬出來，莫名其妙的悲哀
像一隻螃蟹，伸出銳利的前足
緊緊地，箝住我的無名指

我想，明天是否應該
把一株黃色的野菊花
種在瓶口，讓它
長出另一種芬芳？

現代夫妻

我們的愛情居住在石頭裡
大部分的時間是又冷又硬
偶爾碰撞

2

In the deep night, the empty bottle is crying for thirst
Mouth opening, head raising
I can not help yawning

Holding it in my hand
Suddenly I crawl out, namelessly sad
Like a crab, which extends its sharp forelegs
Closely, it pinches my forefingers

I think, whether or not tomorrow
I can plant a wild yellow chrysanthemum
In the bottle, for it
To put out another scent?

Modern Couple

Our love dwells in the stone
Most of the time it is both cold and hard
Occasional clash

也會閃出亮麗而短促的火花
我們為那朵火花命名：
夫妻

有時候我們用石頭雕刻
雕一對鴛鴦
就是雕不出一雙翅膀
讓石頭飛去

不然就在石頭上
鑿出一條條的河流
但是鑿不出水來
有河無水
叫河怎麼去流

此刻，我們不禁落淚
淚水掉在石頭上
乍聞水流聲遠遠奔來

And there is bright and brief sparks
We name the fiery flower:
Couple

Sometimes we carve with a stone
Into a pair of mandarin birds
But fail to carve out a pair of wings
For the stone to fly away

Otherwise on the stone
We carve out one after another river
But fail to carve out water
A river without water
How can a river run

Now, we cannot help shedding tears
Which drop onto the stone
The gurgling of water travels here from afar

洗臉記

那天早晨，當他
端出一盆水準備洗臉
一俯身，突然
臉掉進水裡了

「啊　！」
他驚慌失色地大叫起來
但見臉在水中，搖搖晃晃
漸漸擴大，漸漸碎去

他於是緊張地伸出雙手去撈
撈起來的
卻不是令他日夜懷念的那張臉
而是一陣陣寒意襲來
使他莫名其妙地顫慄不已

匆匆把水潑向曬衣場
仔細地找了老半天什麼也沒發現
他不禁喃喃自問道：「我的臉呢？」

Face Washing

That morning, when he
Gets a basinful of water to wash face
Bending, all of a sudden
My face has dropped into the water

Ah!
He exclaimed in a fluttered manner
The face in the water, is shaking and trembling
Spreading gradually, breaking and fading gradually

And nervously he extends his hands to get it
But what has been caught
Is not the face which he has been missing day and night
With a spell after another spell of chill
He is trembling for no reason

The water is splashed to the clothes-sunning ground in haste
Nothing has been found after careful searching
He cannot help asking himself: "where is my face?"

菩提達摩

達摩把一面鏡子
掛在沉思的墻上
久久一聲不響，終於
他的影子被墻貼了出來

一剎那，生前的本來面目
從鏡裡走向他的沉默中

禪的翅膀
於是把他的思想
飛入
九霄雲外

達摩因此而菩提
即使，苦海茫茫，茫茫無邊
祇要一根蘆葦，輕輕
他便渡過去了

Bodhidharma

Bodhidharma hangs a mirror
On a meditating wall
For a long while no sound, eventually
His shadow has been pasted by the wall

In an instant, the true image before birth
Walks into his silence from the mirror

Therefore the wings of zen
Carry his thought
Beyond
The heaven of heavens

Hence dharma is Bodhi
In spite of the boundless bitter sea, boundless
With only a reed, gently
He swims across it

嘔　吐

　　—— 有一天，他喝得酩酊大醉
　　　　　但是卻很快樂，因為
　　　　　他可以趁機吐掉，吐掉平時
　　　　　不敢吐的東西

睜開眼，天旋地轉
兩路旁的電線桿，向他
猛衝過來
踉蹌倒退三步
閉上眼，清清楚楚地
聽到血液奔流在體內的聲音

醉了吧醉了，真的
他緊緊地摟住淒涼的夜色
他想嘔吐
吐出腸吐出肺
吐出不可說的絕望

Vomiting

— One day, he is dead drunk
　　　But he is joyful, because
　　　He can take the chance to vomit, something
　　　He dares not vomit as his way

Opening the eyes, the sky and earth are turning around
The wire poles by the sides of the road, suddenly dash
Toward him
Staggering back three steps
Eyes closing, clearly
He can hear the blood running within the body

Drunk, drunken, really
Closely he hugs the melancholy night
He wants to vomit
Both his bowls and his lungs
As well as his unspeakable despair

最後撞入浴室
打開嘴巴，打開胸膛
打開冰冷的水龍頭
他興奮地取出腸取出肺
一面唱歌一面洗

Finally he bumps into the bathroom

To open the mouth, open the chest

Open the icy cold faucet

Excitedly he gets out his bowls and lungs

Which he washes while singing

鄭雅文詩選

詩人簡介

　　鄭雅文 Angela Cheng，1954 年 10 月生於臺灣。以第一名考上基隆女中，東吳大學日文系畢業。目前任法易通高級顧問。自幼喜歡閱讀文學作品，從高中時父親贈與的「天地一沙鷗」，開啟了閱讀的興趣，逐步的將生活中的點點滴滴，用文字記錄下來。

　　生活中總有不如意的事情，常會想起印度詩人泰格爾敘述小草的詩，即使是一株小草也能有一片天空，更能給自己力量與勇氣，面對所有困境。

　　大學以後，生活忙碌之間，仍不忘隨筆寫下生活點滴。平時熱愛音樂，收藏各家的經典音樂作品，除此之外更愛拍照，為社團夥伴留念。

工作之餘，熱衷於佛教及各項社會服務，從事非營利組織公益活動已將近二十載。爾後接觸中國文藝協會，更受邀擔任詩報社長、華文現代詩社社長，目前於國際崇她台北一社擔任社長一職(Zonta International District 31, Area 1 Zonta Club of Taipei I President　)。

Selected poems of Angela Cheng

About the Poet

Angela Cheng was born in October, 1954 in Taiwan. She entered Jilong Middle School with her entrance exam scores totaling number one, and she was graduated from the Japanese Department of Soochow University. Currently she is an advanced advisor of Fayitong. She likes reading literary works since her childhood, and her reading interest is enhanced since a book was presented by her father in her senior middle school days, and she writes down the tidbits of her life gradually.

There are some things which are unsatisfactory in our life, which remind us of a poem by Tagore on tender grass. Even a blade of grass has a patch of sky, which encourages us to face up to all difficulties in our life.

After college graduation, she never forgets to jot down

interesting things from her life, in spite of her busy life. As a music lover, she collects classic music pieces by various authors. In addition, she is an ardent lover of photo taking, and she often takes photos for the society.

In her spare time, she has a passion for Buddhism and various social services, and for nearly 20 years she has been engaged in activities by non-profit organization. Then she comes into contact with Chinese Literary Association, and she has been invited to be director of the newspaper office and director of Modern Chinese Poetry Society. Currently she assumes director of a society which is located at Zonta International District 31, Area 1 Zonta Club of Taipei I President.

春之語

白雲憩息在錯落的遠方
微風吹皺了臨溪的花影
城市的喧嘩　歇足
年華的負荷　輕卸

林大蔥翠
為大地彩繪容顏鮮明
花言花語
為人們訴說江山如畫

萌發新芽
源自於土地的脈動
綻放希望
源自於自然的薰陶

入眼的花影蕊姿
一半飄入風中
一半深入心靈

Words of Spring

White clouds perch in the distant places which are high and low
A breeze crumples the flowery shadow of the creek
The noise of the city　　adequate rest
From the burden of years　　unburndened lightly

Big woods emerald
To paint the great earth bright and colorful
Flowery words
Telling people about the picturesque landscape

Buds germinate
From the pulse of the soil
To blossom the hope
From nurture of the nature

Flowery beauty in the eyes
Half into the wind
Half into the soul

天空與大地
依然遙遠無盡
花簇錦團的風景
生意滿盈的氛圍
將無邊的綠意移植上人間淨土

小時候

那些年我們沒有錢
但卻有著快樂童年

小時候
我們沒有 ipad，

不懂 LV
理解不了阿瑪尼。

我們只會
打「昂阿飄」

玩彈珠、打陀螺
彈橡皮筋……

The sky and the earth

Still endless and boundless

The landscape of flowery balls

The atmosphere filled with business

To transplant boundless green into pure land of the mortal world

When Small

In those years we do not have money

But we enjoy a happy childhood

When small

We do not have ipad

No understanding LV

No understanding Armani

We can only play

"Angahpiao"

Play beads, play spinning top

And play rubber string …

那時候
男孩追女孩

一追
就是好幾年

比的是心
念的是一份情

這年頭
男人追女人

幾天就
抱得美人歸

看的是利
拼的是老爹啊！！

以前我們
春遊燒烤地瓜

In those years
A boy runs after a girl

And that
For many years

Heart to heart
Emotion to emotion

In these years
Men run after women

In a few days
They sleep together

For profit
And for their fathers who are powerful!

In those days
We roast potatoes during our spring excursion

坐在一起
談天說地亦幸福。

現在各自
埋頭傳 Line。

生活裡
貌似所有人

都不再
那麼無可取代。

滿口忙事業
已被利益薰心了

愛情、友情
親情，都遺失了

特別懷念那……
美好的純真年代。

Even sitting and talking
Freely we feel joy and happiness

But now we are buried
In our respective Line

In life
It seems that all people

Are no more
Irreplaceable

On the pretext of business
Profit has suffused our heart

Love, friendship
Family emotion, all have been lost

A particular fondness …
For those years which are pure and fair

寧靜午後

一個風和
日麗的午後

搭乘客運穿越
花蓮的海岸山脈

抵達了濱臨
東太平洋的豐濱

惜驟雨聚至
在煙雨濛濛的海邊

遠山近水全
躲進了雲霧中

好不失望！
此時無人煙踏跡

A Quiet Afternoon

An afternoon of gentle
Wind and fair sun

The passengers have been picked up
Over the seaside and mountain of Hualien

Reaching Fengbin
The border of the east Pacific

A pity a heavy rain falls
At the misty seaside

Distant mountains and nearby water
All hide in fog and clouds

How disappointing!
Now no human traces

頗有著：
千山鳥飛絕
萬徑人踪滅
孤舟蓑笠翁
獨釣寒江雪
之景象 YEAH⋯⋯

靜浦位於
台東的小魚港

靜靜的沒有人
幾幢低矮的屋宇

似掉落在
地上的木積

稀疏的散佈在
低矮漆黑的小雜貨店

向看守的
阿婆買了魚罐頭

Here it runs:
Thousands of hills see no flight of birds
Myriads of paths see no human traces
A lonely boat carries a lonely old man
Who is solitarily angling the boundless cold river snow
The landscape YEAH…

Jingpu is a small fishing port
Located in Taidong

It is quiet and there is nobody
A few houses with low eaves

Like the logs which have dropped
Aground from heaven

Low and dark stores
Are sparsely scattered

Fish can has been bought
From the granny on guard

及泡麵沖泡
簡易飽餐一頓

雨還是下著
坐在小雜貨店裡

望著天空
滾滾的濃雲

只有靜默著等待！
老阿婆與我眼神交會

露出了憨厚的
笑容卻無一絲言語

而我卻有著
一絲莫名的愉悅

是感受生命
存在而感動吧！！

When the instant noodle has been immersed in water
A simple adequate meal

The rain is still falling
Sitting in a small grocery store

Looking at the sky
The heavy clouds on the rolling

Only silently waiting!
Eyes meeting between me and the old granny

Simplicity and naivety have been revealed
With smile but without a single word

But I have a slight
Joy which is nameless

To feel life
Existence and be moved!

樂　活

光陰似箭轉眼
已邁入不惑之年

細微之瑣事
如今也非關緊要

樂活是目標
幸福似感覺了

能慷慨解囊
亦是一種樂趣

地位是暫時的
榮耀是過去的

健康是自己的
才德兼備又怎樣

Joy

Time flies like an arrow in an instant
I am over forty years of age

Fine trivialities
Now are no more important

Joy is our target
Happiness is like a feeling

To be generous in giving
Is also a joy

The position is temporary
The glory is past

Health is our own concern
Virtue plus talent so

不圖回報
唯有世上雙親

父母對子女的
視為義務和樂趣

以寬闊的胸襟
迎接那璀璨的朝陽

珍惜已擁有的
欣賞周遭人事物

調整我們的心態
亦享受快樂人生

No intention for retribution
Only parents in the world

The parents' love for their children
Is taken as a duty and joy

With a bosom of breadth and width
To greet the brilliant morning sun

Cherish what is now in hands
Appreciate things and people about us

Adjust our frame of mind
To enjoy a happy life

山居歲月

人生精彩並非數字
是那些動人的故事

馳騁在蜿蜒的回家路
心境隨著時空轉換

在綠色走廊上奔馳
假日相伴漫步林間

庭院赤腳體驗草皮
觸感認識鳳蝶樹蛙

讓大自然成為孩子
最好的人生指導師

留下一面開窗權利
留下呼吸天地大窗

Years of Life in the Mountain

Life is brilliant not with numbers
It is those moving stories

Galloping on the zigzag road back home
The frame of mind changes with time and space

Running on the green corridor
On holidays in company strolling in woods

In the courtyard barefooted to experience the turf
To recognize butterflies and tree frogs

For the nature to be children
The best tutor in life

Reserve the right to open the window
Leave the big window of heaven and earth for breath

居住山林植被豐富
空氣中的懸浮粒子

大量芬多精養護著
潛移默化加值成效

自然空調全年無休
吸氣都含氧的淨化

養生不費吹灰之力
為人生寫下新樂章

The mountain woods boast a rich plantation
Floating grains in the air

A lot of things to be nurtured
To be effective gradually and stealthily

The natural air conditioner does not rest all year round
Even breathing is purified with oxygen

It is very easy to keep a good health
New chapters about life have been written

劉正偉詩選

作者簡介

劉正偉，文學博士。現為台客文化協會理事長、桃園市美術協會理事、《台客》詩刊總編輯、《華文現代詩》詩刊編委、野薑花詩社顧問，《詩人俱樂部》FB 網站創辦人，國立台北大學、海洋大學兼任助理教授。

曾獲：全國優秀青年詩人獎、苗栗縣夢花文學獎新詩首獎、2016 國史館台灣文獻館學術著作優等獎等。2015 雲林縣文化處草嶺創作者計畫油畫得主。

著有詩集：《我曾看見妳眼角的憂傷》、《詩路漫漫》、《貓貓雨──劉正偉詩選》等七本。編著：《早期藍星詩史》、《覃子豪詩研究》等。

Selected Poems of Liu Chengwei

About the author

Liu Zhengwei is doctor of literature. Now he is president of Tai Ke Cultural Association, president of Fine Arts Association of Taoyuan City, editor-in-chief of the poetry periodical entitled *Taike*, editor of *Chinese Modern Poetry Quarterly*, advisor of Yejianghua poetry editorial office, founder of *Poets Club* FB network, part-time professor of National Taipei University and the Ocean University.

He has ever won a lot of prizes: prize for national excellent young poets, the first prize for new poetry of literary prizes of Miaoli County, and prize for 2016 excellent academic monographs, etc. And in 2015 he won prize for his oil painting in Yunlin County.

He has published 7 poetry collections, including *I Have Seen Your Sorrowful Eyes*, *Long and Lengthy Poetry*

Road, Drizzling Rain — Selected Poems of Liu Zhengwei, etc. In addition, he has compiled some books such as *The Poetry History of Early Blue Star* and *Research on the Poetry of Qin Zihao,* etc.

思　念

將情緒捐給白雲
讓她帶走一些煩憂
將時間捐給睡眠
讓她帶走一些疲憊
將眺望捐給星空
讓她帶走一些思念

然而，將捐什麼給妳？
才能表達我深深的眷戀
於是，我將一些思念捐給妳
好讓妳思念，我的思念

Missing

Donate emotion to white clouds
For her to take away some worries
Donate time to sleep
For her to take away some weariness
Donate distant gazing to the starry sky
For her to take away some missing

However, what to be donated to you?
So as to express my profound yearning
Therefore, I donate some missing to you
For you to miss, my missing

給我遠方的姑娘

一句輕聲道別
影子，就越拉越長了
像遠方朦朧的山頭
依然，記得妳的眸似星子
髮似流雲，唇似野火
膚似初雪，頰似蘋果
眉，卻深深深鎖

深鎖腦海中的還有，嚶嚶
柔情似水的呢呢細語
像整夜滴滴答答不寐的雨滴

給我遠方的姑娘
衾枕被褥就要乾了
快快回到我的臂彎
草要綠了，花要開了
春天，就要來了

To My Girl Far Away

A gentle farewell
The shadow, becomes longer and longer
Like the dim distant mountaintop
Still, I remember your star-like eyes
Your hair is like floating clouds, lips like wild fire
Your skin like the first snow, your cheeks like an apple
And your brows, are closely knit

What is locked deep in your mind, murmuring
The soft whispers with tender feelings
Like the raindrops which drip and drop throughout the night

To my girl afar
The quilt and pillow is to dry up
Be quick to return to my arms
The grass is to green, flowers are to bloom
Spring, is around the corner

長城懷古

一腳就跨上歷史的顛峰
多少皇朝賴以苟延的屏障
苔痕是血淚和歲月不斷爭戰的象徵
撫視時間被遺忘而傾圮的角落

變幻的是城垛兩岸輪迴的風景四季
千年不變的是南方草原不斷滋養的風風雨雨
回首來時的道路坎坷依舊
前面的路途卻叢生草雜

啊！遠處的烽火台
據說毀於吳三桂守關那一年
如今，誰來？擎起微弱的火炬
點燃千年不舉的狼煙

所謂豐功偉業？成就了多少梟雄
在教科書裡不斷殺進殺出
好漢絡繹於途
而英雄，早已滾落歷史的長城

Reminiscence on the Great Wall

One step and it is the peak of history
The protective screen by which many imperial dynasties
    continue to exist
The moss print is the symbol of the incessant war of blood
    and tears and years
Looking at the dilapidated corner where time has forgotten

What is changing is the scenic four seasons to the two
    sides of the wall
What never changes through thousands of years is the
    winds and rains to nurture the southern grassland
Looking back at the road which is bumpy and circuitous
The road ahead is choked with weed

Ah! The smoke towers afar
It is said that it was destroyed during the warring year of
    Wu Sangui
Now, who? To raise the weak torch
To enkindle the wolf-smoke column which disappears for
    thousands of years

The so-called great achievements? How many heroes have
    been created?
Into and out of the textbook to kill
Good men are on the way
And heroes, have already fallen out of the Great Wall of
    history

夜色

在夢不能到達的角落
太陽剛剛熄燈
酒吧裡的月色迫不及待的亮起
孩子們盡情用熱舞揮灑青春
以威士忌灌醉孤獨
寂寞誘惑寂寞
催情的親蜜戰友
由甜言和蜜語粉墨登場

清晨五點三十七分
身為清潔隊員的母親
在街頭酒店轉角的巷口
輕輕
掃起一堆女兒昨夜吐露的真言

The Night

In the corner where the dream fails to reach

The sun has just turned out its lamp

The moon in the bar is impatient to be enkindled

The children waste their youth with hot dance with abandon

With whiskey to drink solitude drunk

Loneliness solicits loneliness

The close comerades-in-arms

Sail onto the stage with honeyed words

At 5: 37 of the morning

As a cleaner Mother

In the lane of the wineshop

Gently

Sweep a pile of true words vomited by her daughter last night

蠡澤湖畔

蠡澤湖畔一塊塊鏗鏘的詩碑
吸引湖岸求偶的蛙聲
爭先躍出水面，跳過風聲蕭蕭
扯開嗓門，紛紛吟哦起來

月光是閃閃發亮的詩句
湖面泛起一道道漣漪
星星也沒閒著
撲通撲通跳下水
蠡澤湖，就更綺麗了

‧蠡澤湖為明道大學著名的校園美景。

By Lize Lake

By Lize Lake one after another poetry stone tablet
To allure the croaking of frogs for mating by the lake
First leaping out of water, then through swishing wind
In a hoarse voice, sing aloud

The moonlight is the bright and brilliant poetic line
The lake is trembling with one after another ripple
The stars are not idle
They plop into water
And Lize Lake, is more beautiful

> • Lize Lake is a beautiful scenic spot on the campus of Mingdao Univeristy.